EASIEST KEYBOARD COLLECTION

90s Hits

WISE PUBLICATIONS
London/New York/Paris/Sydney/Copenhagen/Madrid

Exclusive Distributors:

Music Sales Limited
8/9 Frith Street,
London W1V 5TZ, England.

Music Sales Pty Limited
120 Rothschild Avenue,
Rosebery, NSW 2018,
Australia..

Order No. AM944229
ISBN 0-7119-6606-0
This book © Copyright 1997 by Wise Publications

Cover design by Chloë Alexander
Compiled by Peter Evans
Music arranged by Derek Jones
Music processed by Paul Ewers Music Design

Printed in the United Kingdom by
Caligraving Limited, Thetford, Norfolk.

Cover photograph courtesy of:
The Stock Market

Your Guarantee of Quality
As publishers, we strive to produce every book to the highest commercial
standards.
The music has been freshly engraved and the book has been carefully
designed to minimise awkward page turns and to make playing from it a
real pleasure.
Particular care has been given to specifying acid-free, neutral-sized paper
made from pulps which have not been elemental chlorine bleached. This
pulp is from farmed sustainable forests and was produced with special
regard for the environment.
Throughout, the printing and binding have been planned to ensure a
sturdy, attractive publication which should give years of enjoyment.
If your copy fails to meet our high standards, please inform us and we will
gladly replace it.

Music Sales' complete catalogue describes thousands of titles and is
available in full colour sections by subject, direct from Music Sales
Limited. Please state your areas of interest and send a cheque/postal
order for £1.50 for postage to: Music Sales Limited, Newmarket Road,
Bury St. Edmunds, Suffolk IP33 3YB.

Visit the Internet Music Shop at
http://www.musicsales.co.uk

Contents

A WHOLE NEW WORLD
(ALADDIN'S THEME)
(From Walt Disney's "Aladdin")

Music by Alan Menken
Lyrics by Tim Rice

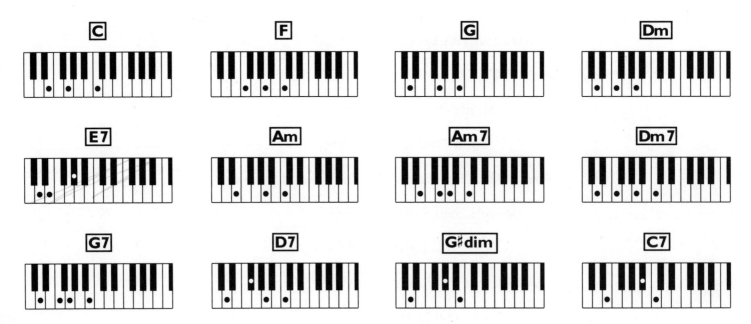

Voice: **Flute**

Rhythm: **Ballad**

Tempo: ♩ = 88

I can show you the world, shin - ning, shim - mer - ing,

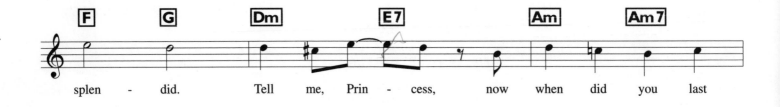

splen - did. Tell me, Prin - cess, now when did you last

let your heart de - cide? I can o - pen your eyes,

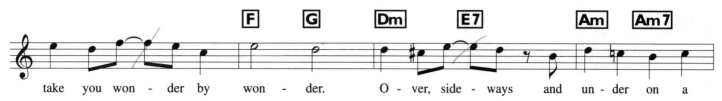

take you won - der by won - der. O - ver, side - ways and un - der on a

ma - gic car - pet ride.___ A whole new___ world,_____

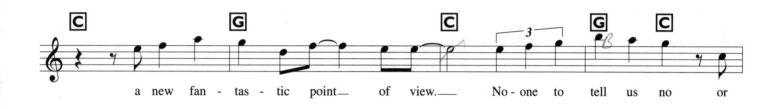

a new fan - tas - tic point___ of view.___ No - one to tell us no or

where to go___ or say we're on - ly___ dream - ing. A whole new world,

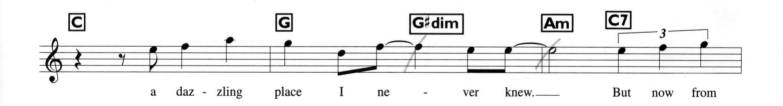

a daz - zling place I ne - ver knew.___ But now from

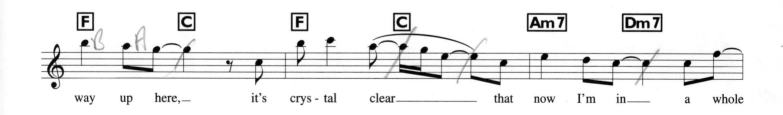

way up here,___ it's crys - tal clear_____ that now I'm in___ a whole

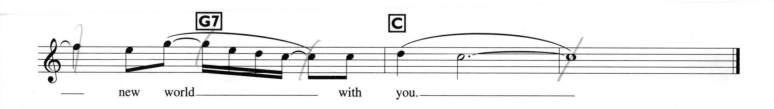

___ new world_____ with you._____

ALWAYS

Words & Music by Jon Bon Jovi
© Copyright 1994 Jon Bon Jovi Publishing, USA.
PolyGram Music Publishing Limited, 47 British Grove, London W4.
All Rights Reserved. International Copyright Secured.

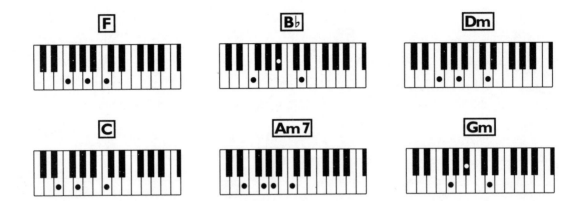

Voice: **Clarinet**

Rhythm: **Ballad**

Tempo: ♩ **= 70**

This Ro - me - o   is bleed - ing,

but you can't see his   blood,—   it's no-thing but some feel-ings   that this old— dog   kicked up.——

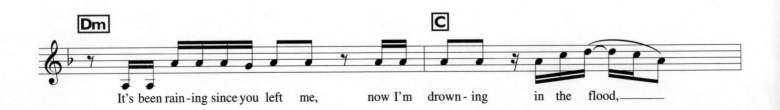

It's been rain-ing since you left   me,   now I'm drown-ing   in the flood,——

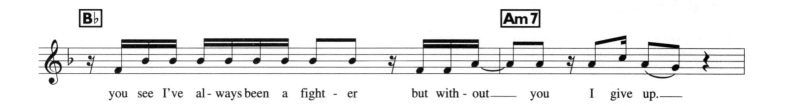

you see I've al-ways been a fight-er but with-out—— you I give up.——

Now I can't sing a love song like the way it's meant to be,—— well I

guess I'm not that good a-ny-more,—— but ba-by that's—— just me.—— Yeah,

I will love—— you ba - by,—— al - ways and I'll be there for -

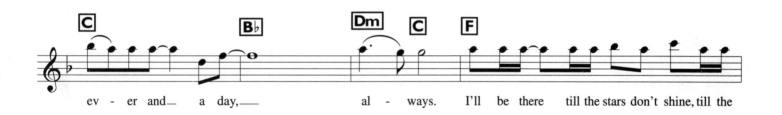

ev - er and—— a day,—— al - ways. I'll be there till the stars don't shine, till the

hea - vens burst—— and the words don't rhyme, I know when I die—— you'll be on my mind and I'll

Repeat to fade

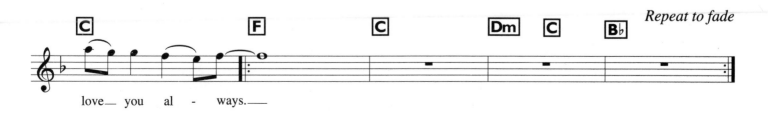

love—— you al - ways.——

AROUND THE WORLD

Words & Music by Mortimer, Harvey, Rowebottom & Stannard
© Copyright 1994 Porky Publishing/PolyGram Music Publishing Limited, 47 British Grove, London W4.
All Rights Reserved. International Copyright Secured.

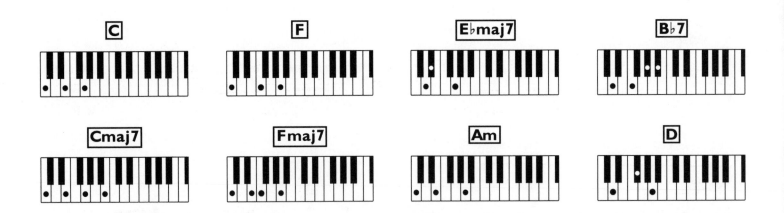

Voice: **Saxophone**

Rhythm: **Soul Ballad**

Tempo: ♩ = 88

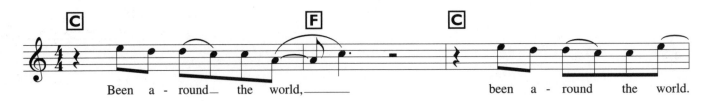

Been a - round— the world,_____ been a - round the world.

Seen the seas, se - ven, sailed a - cross them all.—

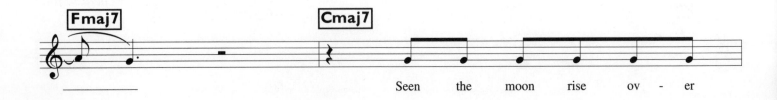

_____ Seen the moon rise ov - er

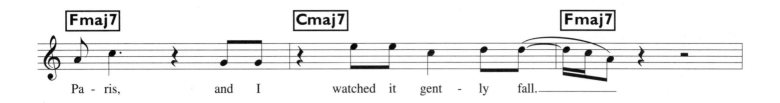

Pa - ris, and I watched it gent - ly fall.—

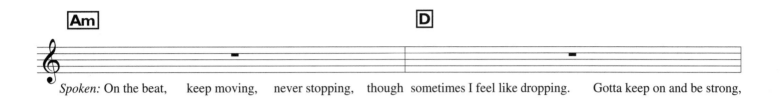

Spoken: On the beat, keep moving, never stopping, though sometimes I feel like dropping. Gotta keep on and be strong,

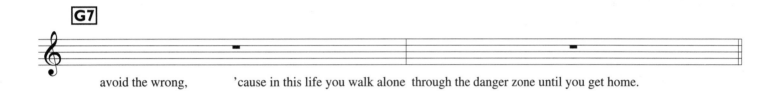

avoid the wrong, 'cause in this life you walk alone through the danger zone until you get home.

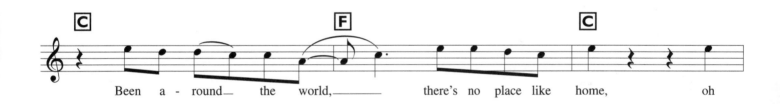

Been a - round— the world,——— there's no place like home, oh

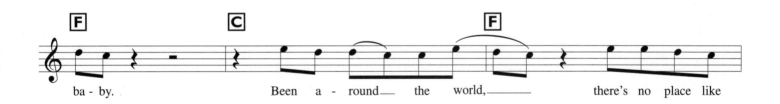

ba - by. Been a - round— the world,——— there's no place like

home, oh ba - by. Take me

home, where my soul be - longs.

(EVERYTHING I DO) I DO IT FOR YOU

Words by Bryan Adams & Robert John 'Mutt' Lange
Music by Michael Kamen

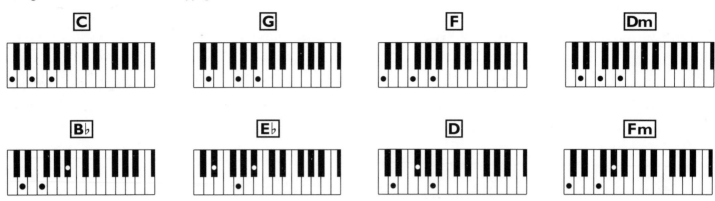

Voice: **Strings**

Rhythm: **Soft Rock**

Tempo: ♩ = 76

Look in-to my eyes, you will see, what you mean to

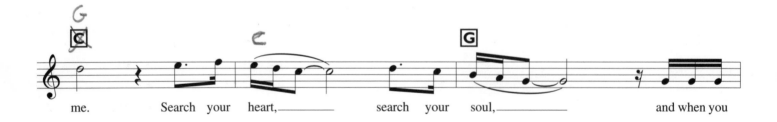

me. Search your heart, search your soul, and when you

find me there you'll search no more. Don't tell me it's not worth try-in'

for, you can't tell me it's not worth dy-in' for. You know it's

true,_____ ev-'ry-thing I do, I do it for— you. There's

no love, like your love and no oth-er could give more love. There's no - where_____ un-less

you're there all the time,_____ all the way,— yeah._____

Oh you can't tell me it's not worth try - in'

for, I can't help____ it, there's no-thin' I want more. Yeah— I would fight for you, I'd

lie for you,— walk the wire for you,— yeah, I'd die for you._____ You know it's

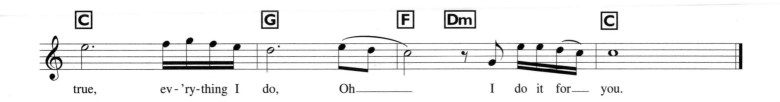

true, ev-'ry-thing I do, Oh_____ I do it for— you.

FIELDS OF GOLD

Words & Music by Sting

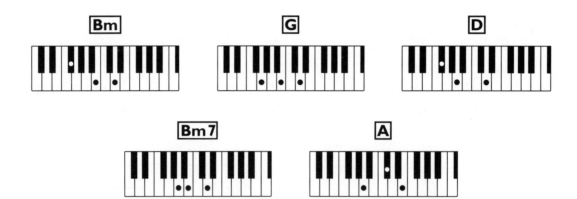

Voice: **Clarinet**

Rhythm: **Soft Rock**

Tempo: ♩ = 96

You'll re - mem - ber me,____ when the

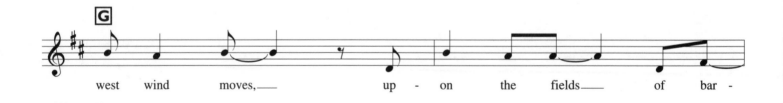

west wind moves,____ up - on the fields____ of bar -

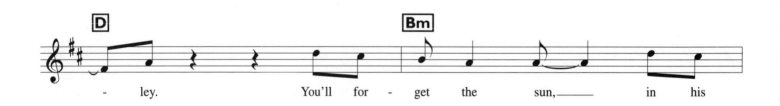

- ley. You'll for - get the sun,____ in his

jea - lous sky,____ as we walk in fields____ of gold.

So she took her love,___ for to gaze a - while,___ up -

- on the fields___ of bar - - ley. In his

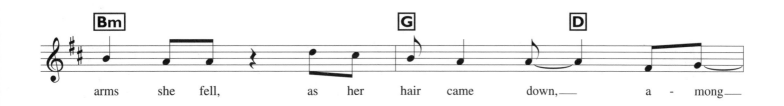

arms she fell, as her hair came down,___ a - mong___

___ the fields___ of gold. When___ we

walked in fields___ of gold.___ When we

walked in fields___ of gold.___

GOOD ENOUGH

Words & Music by Nigel Clark, Mathew Priest & Andy Miller

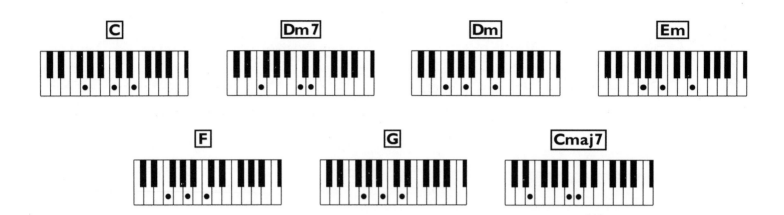

Voice: **Saxophone**

Rhythm: **Rock**

Tempo: ♩ = 116

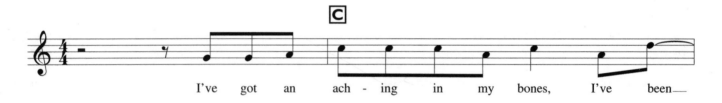

I've got an ach - ing in my bones, I've been

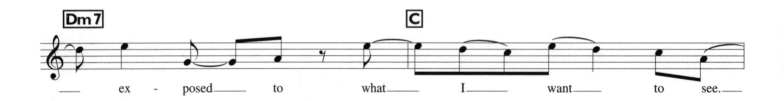

ex - posed to what I want to see.

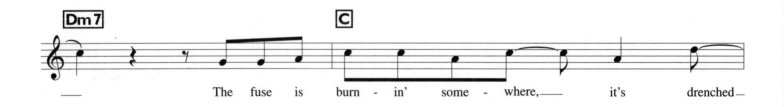

The fuse is burn - in' some - where, it's drenched

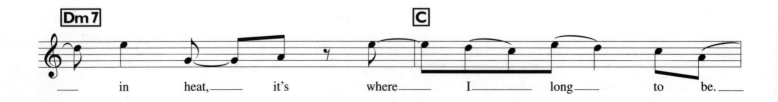

in heat, it's where I long to be.

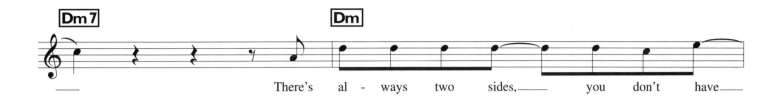

There's al - ways two sides,_____ you don't have_____

_____ to suf - fer, if this is hea - ven then send me_____ to

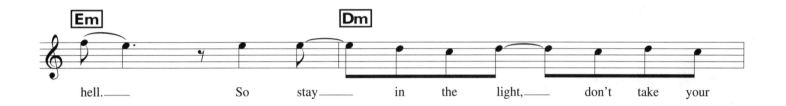

hell._____ So stay_____ in the light,_____ don't take your

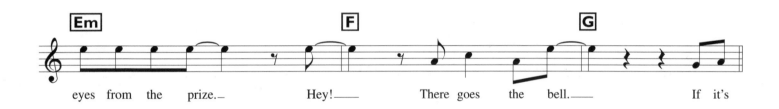

eyes from the prize._ Hey!_____ There goes the bell._____ If it's

good e - nough for you, it's good_____ e - nough for me. If it's good_____ e - nough it's true, it's what_

_____ I want to see. If it's good e - nough for you, it's good_____ e - nough for me. If it's good

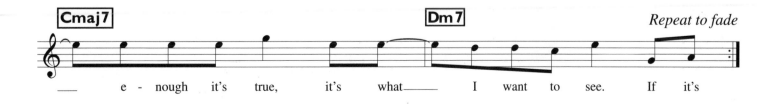

_____ e - nough it's true, it's what_____ I want to see. If it's

Repeat to fade

HAVE I TOLD YOU LATELY

Words & Music by Van Morrison

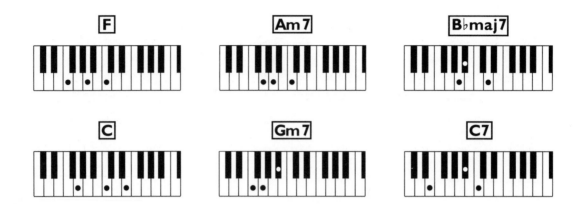

Voice: **Flute**

Rhythm: **Ballad**

Tempo: ♩ = 80

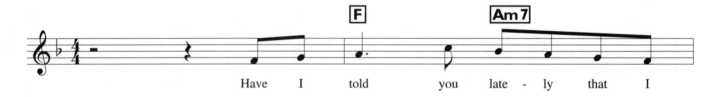

Have I told you late-ly that I

love —— you, —— have I told you there's no - one a -

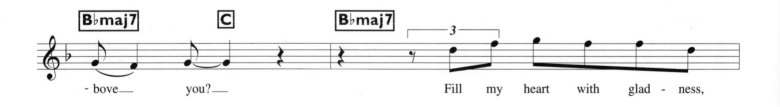

- bove —— you? —— Fill my heart with glad - ness,

take a - way my sad - ness, ease my trou - bles that's what you do.

There's a love that's di - vine and it's yours and it's mine, like the

sun.

At the end of the day, we should give thanks and pray to the one.

Have I told you late - ly that I love you,

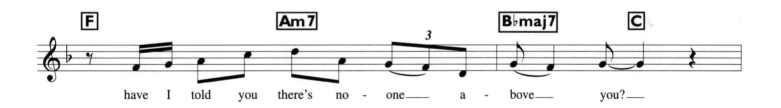

have I told you there's no - one a - bove you?

Fill my heart with glad - ness, take a - way my sad - ness,

ease my trou - bles that's what you do.

HOW DEEP IS YOUR LOVE

Words & Music by Barry Gibb, Robin Gibb & Maurice Gibb

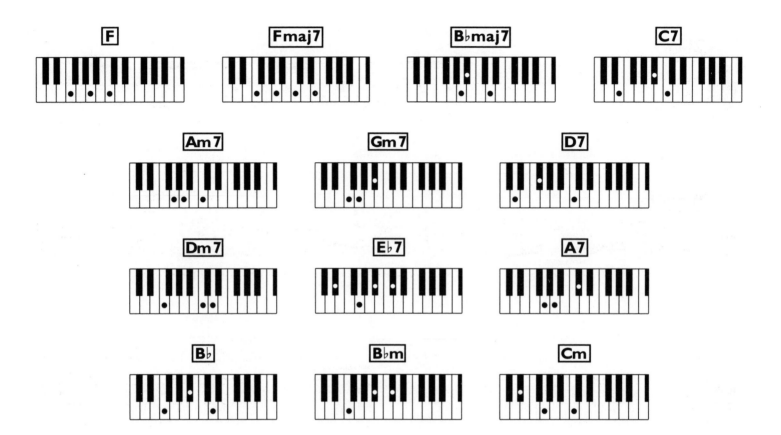

Voice:	**Saxophone**
Rhythm:	**Soft Rock**
Tempo:	♩ = 88

I know your

eyes in the morn-ing sun,___ I feel you touch___ me in the pour-ing rain.___ And the mo-

-ment that you wan-der far___ from me,___ I wan-na feel you in my arms a-gain.

___ And you come___ to me___ on a Sum - mer breeze;___ keep me warm

___ in your love,___ then you soft - ly leave.___ And it's me you need___ to show:___ How deep

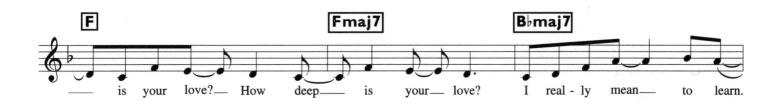

___ is your love?___ How deep___ is your___ love? I real - ly mean___ to learn.

_____ 'Cause we're liv - ing in a world of fools,___ break - ing us

down when they all_____ should let us be.___ We be - long___

___ to you___ and me.___

I BELIEVE

Words & Music by Ervin Drake, Irvin Graham,
Jimmy Shirl & Al Stillman

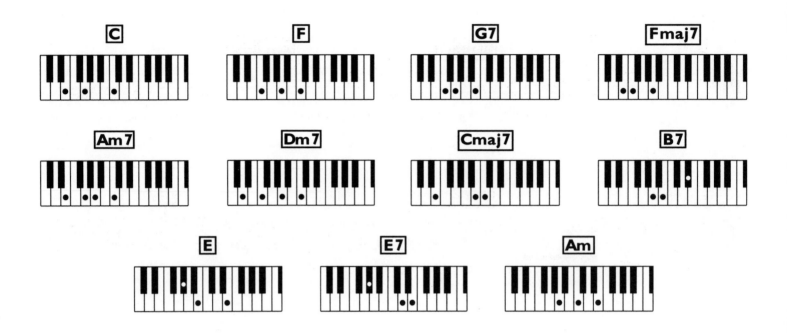

Voice: **Trumpet**

Rhythm: **Ballad**

Tempo: ♩ = 90

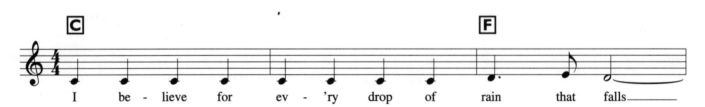

I be - lieve for ev - 'ry drop of rain that falls_____

_____ a flow - er grows._____ I be - lieve that

some - where in the dark - est night_____ a can - dle

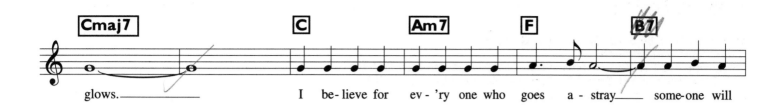

glows. _____ I be-lieve for ev-'ry one who goes a-stray____ some-one will

come_____ to show the way._____ I be-lieve,____ I

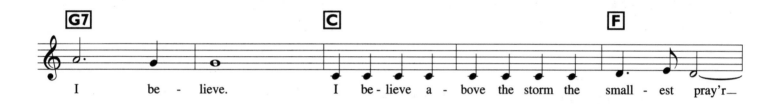

I be-lieve. I be-lieve a-bove the storm the small-est pray'r___

____ will still be heard._____ I be-lieve that some-one in the

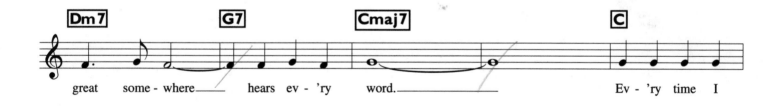

great some-where____ hears ev-'ry word._____ Ev-'ry time I

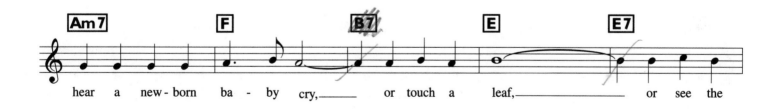

hear a new-born ba-by cry,____ or touch a leaf,_____ or see the

sky,_____ then I know why I be-lieve.____

I WILL ALWAYS LOVE YOU

Words & Music by Dolly Parton

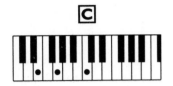  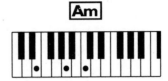 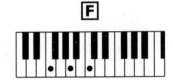

Voice: **Ocarina**

Rhythm: **Ballad**

Tempo: ♩ = 76

If I should—

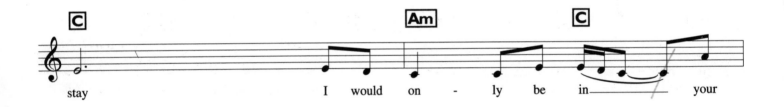

stay   I would on - ly be in your

way,   so I'll go,   but I

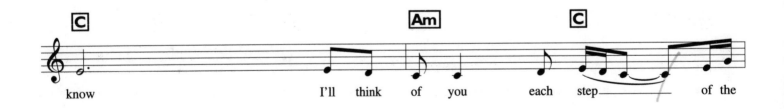

know   I'll think of you each step of the

way.   And I   will

KEEP THE FAITH

Words & Music by Jon Bon Jovi, Richie Sambora & Desmond Child
© Copyright 1992 PolyGram International Music Incorporated/Bon Jovi Publishing/Aggressive Music/
EMI April Music Incorporated/Desmobile Music Company, USA.
EMI Songs Limited, 127 Charing Cross Road, London WC2 (33.33%)/
PolyGram Music Publishing Limited, 47 British Grove, London W4 (66.66%).
All Rights Reserved. International Copyright Secured.

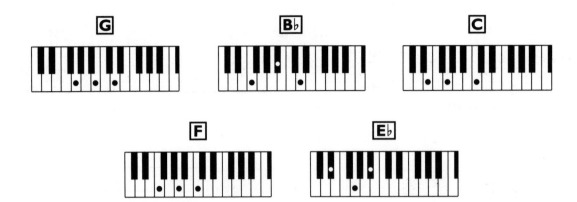

Voice: **Saxophone**

Rhythm: **Soft Rock**

Tempo: ♩ = 92

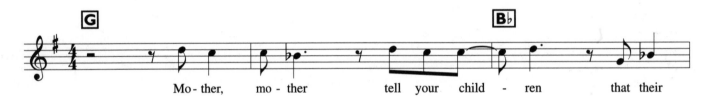

Mo - ther,   mo - ther   tell your child - ren   that their

time has just — be - gun. _____   I have suf - fered   for my

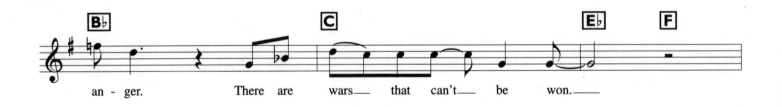

an - ger.   There are wars — that can't — be won. ____

Ev - 'ry - bo - dy needs some - bo - dy to love, —   ev - 'ry - bo - dy needs some-

-bo - dy to hate.____ Ev - 'ry - bo - dy's bitch - ing 'cause they

can't get e - nough____ and it's hard____ to hold on____ when there's no -

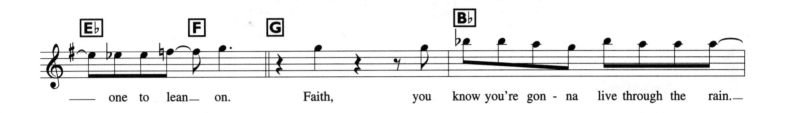

____ one to lean____ on. Faith, you know you're gon - na live through the rain.____

____ Lord____ you got to keep the faith.____ Faith,

don't you let your love turn to hate,____ now____ we got to keep the faith.__

____ Faith, keep the faith,____ keep the faith.____

Repeat to fade

_____ Lord we got to keep the faith.____

LOVE IS ALL AROUND

Words & Music by Reg Presley
© Copyright 1967 Dick James Music Limited, 47 British Grove, London W4.
All Rights Reserved. International Copyright Secured.

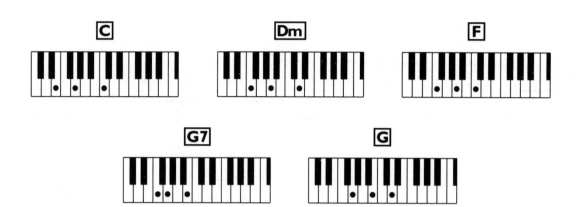

Voice: **Ocarina**

Rhythm: **Soft Rock**

Tempo: ♩ = 85

I feel it in my fin-gers,   I feel it in my   toes.—

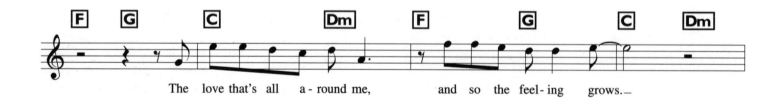

The love that's all a-round me,   and so the feel-ing   grows.—

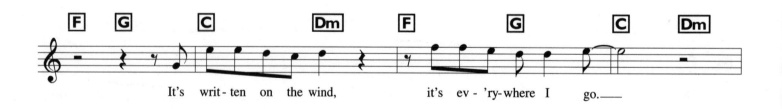

It's writ-ten on the wind,   it's ev-'ry-where I   go.—

So if you real-ly love me,   come on and let it   show.—

You know I love you, I al - ways — will, —

my mind's made up by the way that I feel. — There's no be - gin - ning, there'll

be no — end, — 'cause on my — love — you can de - pend. — It's

writ - ten in — the wind — oh, — ev - 'ry where I go. —

So if you real - ly love me, come on and let it

show. — Come on and let it show.
Come on and let — it,

Repeat to fade

come on and let — it, come on and let — it show. —

27

MORE THAN WORDS

Words & Music by Nuno Bettencourt & Gary Cherone

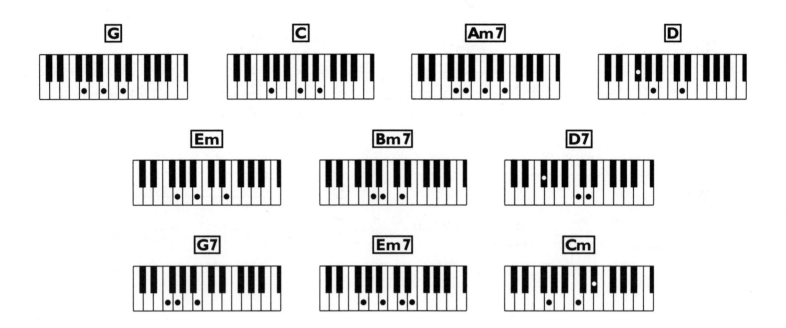

Voice: **Saxophone**

Rhythm: **Soft Rock**

Tempo: ♩ = 88

Say - ing 'I___ love___ you' is not the words___ I want___

___ to___ hear___ from you.___ It's not that I___ want___ you

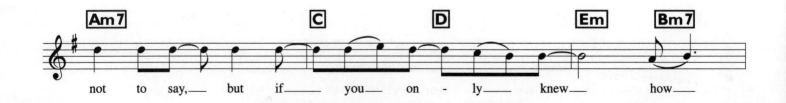

not to say,___ but if___ you on - ly___ knew___ how___

ea - sy____ it would be____ to____ show____ me how____ you feel,____

____ more than words_____ is all you have____ to____ do____

____ to make____ it____ real.____ Then you would - n't have____ to say____

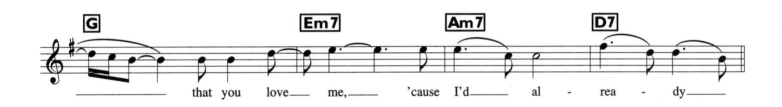

_____ that you love____ me,____ 'cause I'd____ al - rea - dy____

know. What would you say____ if I took____

____ those words____ a - way,____ then you could - n't make_____ things new____

____ just by say - ing 'I____ love____ you'.

ONE SWEET DAY

Words & Music by Mariah Carey, Walter Afanasieff,
Shawn Stockman, Michael McCary, Nathan Morris & Wanya Morris

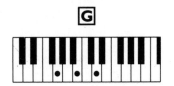
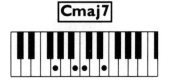
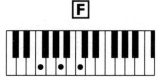

Voice: **Clarinet**

Rhythm: **Ballad**

Tempo: ♩ = 80

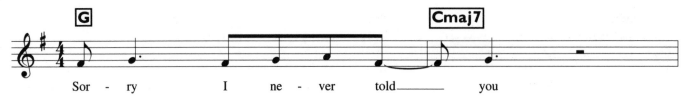

Sor - ry I ne - ver told_____ you

all I want - ed to say._____ And

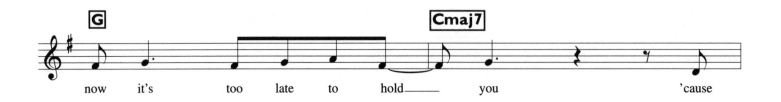

now it's too late to hold_____ you 'cause

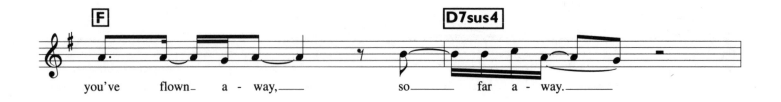

you've flown___ a - way,_____ so_____ far a - way.

Ne - ver had I i - ma - - - gined_____

living_____ with - out your smile._____

Feel - ing_____ and know - ing you hear_____ me,_____ it keeps

me a - live,_____ a - live._____ And I

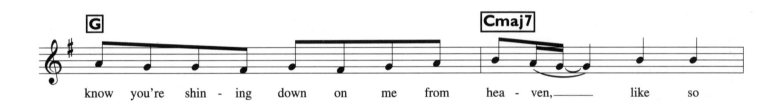

know you're shin - ing down on me from hea - ven,_____ like so

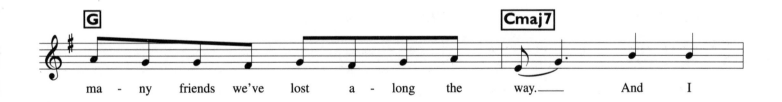

ma - ny friends we've lost a - long the way._____ And I

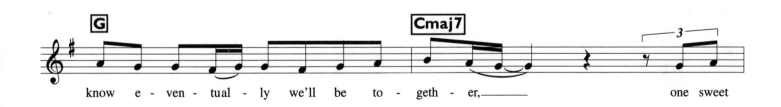

know e - ven - tual - ly we'll be to - geth - er,_____ one sweet

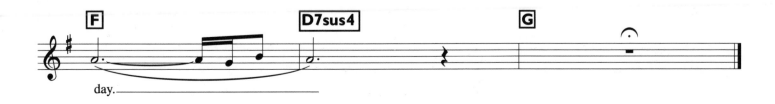

day._____

SAY YOU'LL BE THERE

Words & Music by Eliot Kennedy, Melanie Brown, Victoria Aadams,
Geri Halliwell, Emma Bunton & Melanie Chisholm
© Copyright 1996 Sony/ATV Music Publishing, 10 Great Marlborough Street, London W1 (50%)
& Windswept Pacific Music Limited, 27 Queensdale Place, London W11 (50%).
All Rights Reserved. International Copyright Secured.

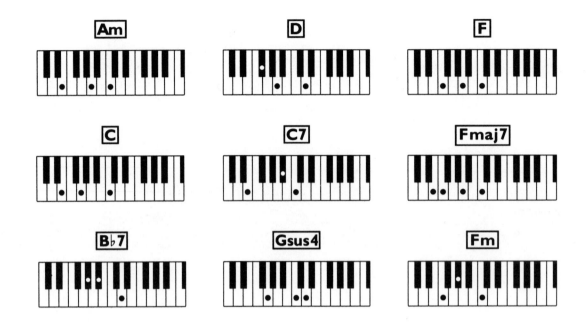

Voice: **Clarinet**

Rhythm: **Soul Ballad**

Tempo: ♩ = 108

Last time, that we had this con-ver-sa-tion,

I de-ci-ded we should be friends. But now we're

go-ing round in cir-cles, tell me will this dé-jà vu nev-er end.

Now you tell me that you've fall-en in love,___ well I ne-

-ver, ev-er thought that would be.___ This time you

got-ta take__ it ea-sy, throw-ing far too much e-mo-tion at me,___ but a-ny fool

___ can see__ they're fall - ing, I got-ta make you un - der - stand.

___ I'm giv-ing you ev - ery - thing,___ all that joy___

___ can bring,__ this I swear.___ And all that I want

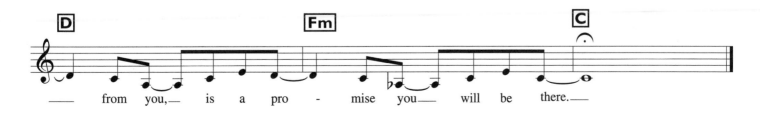

___ from you,__ is a pro - mise you__ will be there.___

TEARS IN HEAVEN

Words & Music by Eric Clapton & Will Jennings
© Copyright 1991 & 1997 E.C. Music Limited, London NW1 (87.5%).
© Copyright 1991 Blue Sky Rider Songs administered by Rondor Music (London) Limited,
10a Parsons Green, London SW6 for the World (excluding USA & Canada) (12.5%).
All Rights Reserved. International Copyright Secured.

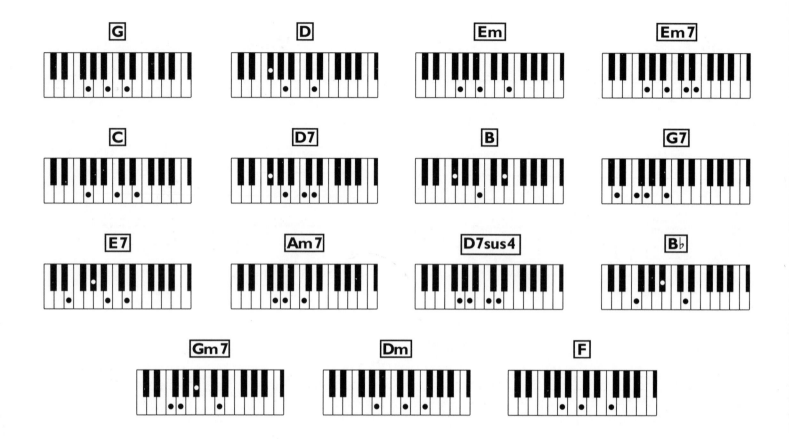

Voice:　**Oboe**

Rhythm:　**Soft Rock**

Tempo:　♩ = 80

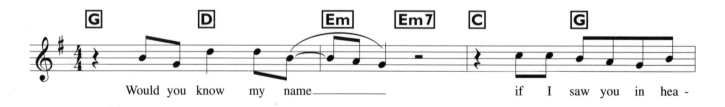

Would you know my name_____ if I saw you in hea-

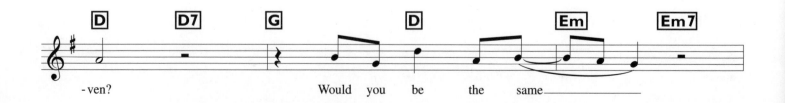

-ven?　Would you be the same_____

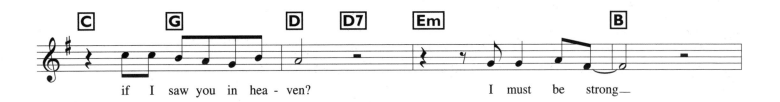

if I saw you in hea - ven?   I must be strong—

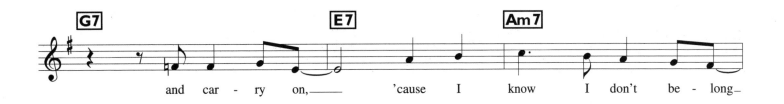

and car - ry on,—— 'cause I know I don't be - long—

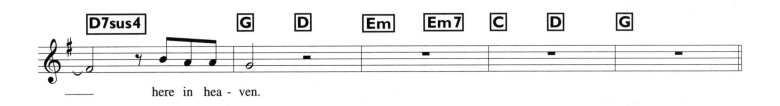

—— here in hea - ven.

Time can bring you down,—— time can bend your knees.——

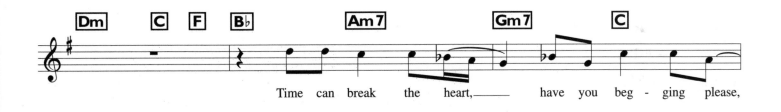

Time can break the heart,—— have you beg - ging please,

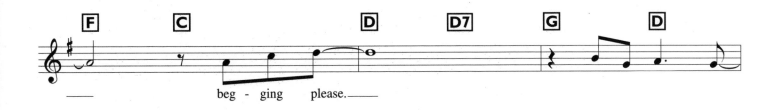

—— beg - ging please.——

2 BECOME 1

Words & Music by Matt Rowe, Richard Stannard, Melanie Brown,
Victoria Aadams, Geri Halliwell, Emma Bunton & Melanie Chisholm

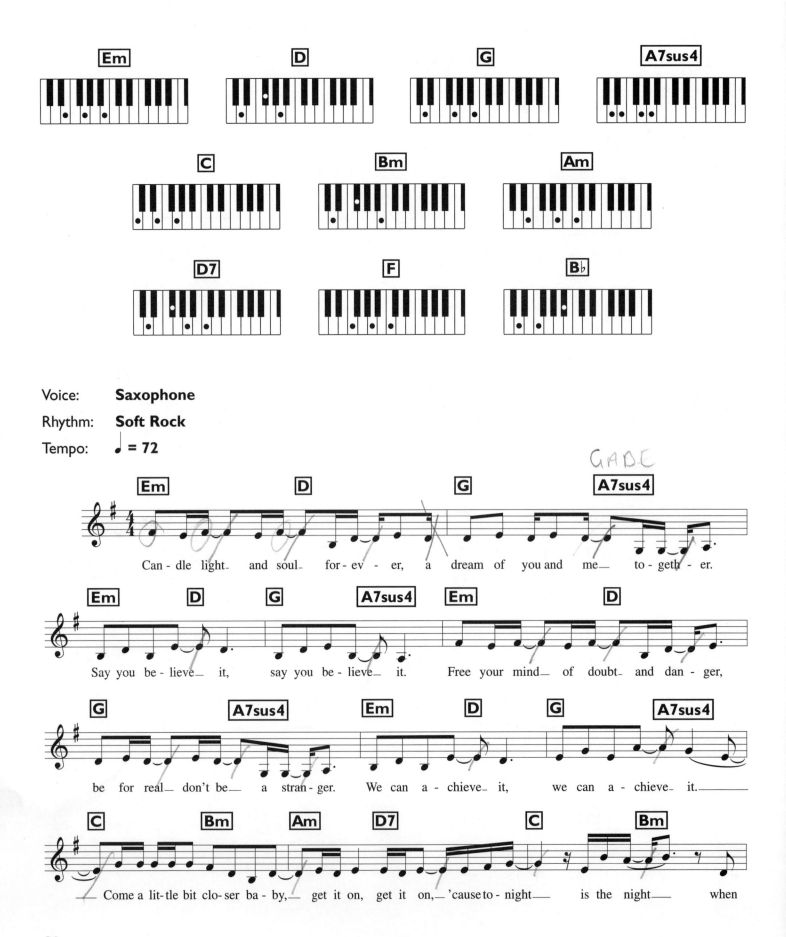

Voice: **Saxophone**

Rhythm: **Soft Rock**

Tempo: ♩ = 72

Can - dle light_ and soul_ for - ev - er, a dream of you and me_ to - geth - er.

Say you be - lieve_ it, say you be - lieve_ it. Free your mind_ of doubt_ and dan - ger,

be for real_ don't be_ a stran - ger. We can a - chieve_ it, we can a - chieve_ it.____

_ Come a lit - tle bit clo - ser ba - by,_ get it on, get it on,_ 'cause to - night_ is the night_ when

UNCHAINED MELODY

Music by Alex North
Words by Hy Zaret

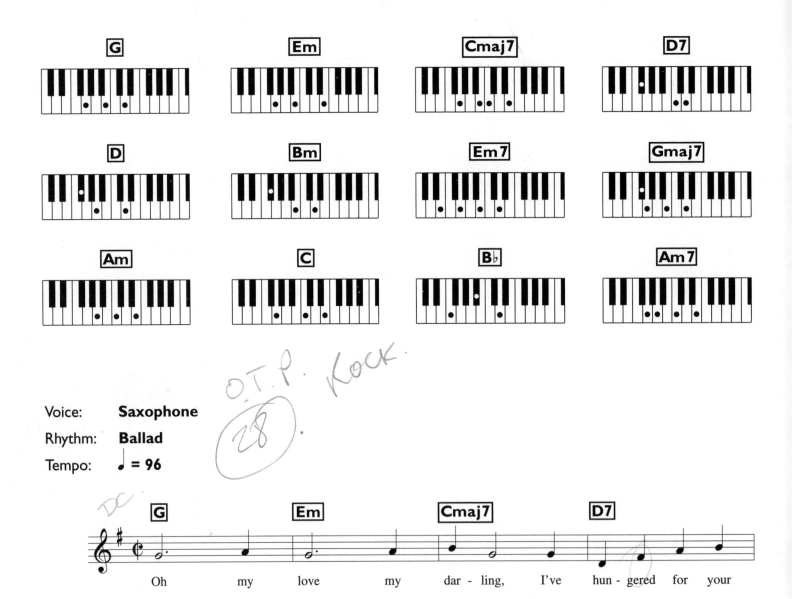

Voice: **Saxophone**
Rhythm: **Ballad**
Tempo: ♩ = 96

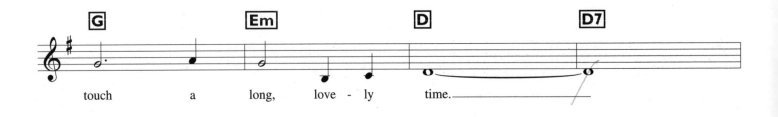

Oh my love my dar - ling, I've hun - gered for your

touch a long, love - ly time. _____

Time goes by so slow - ly and time can do so

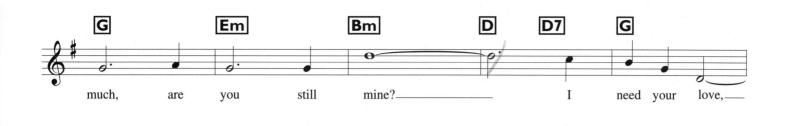

much, are you still mine?_____ I need your love,_____

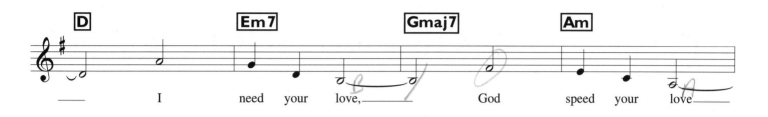

_____ I need your love,_____ God speed your love_____

FINE.

to me!_____ Lone - ly ri - vers

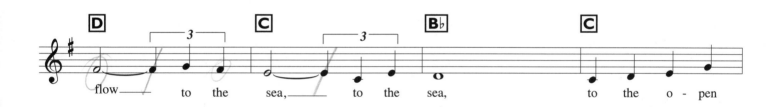

flow_____ to the sea,_____ to the sea, to the o - pen

arms_____ of the sea. Lone - ly ri - vers

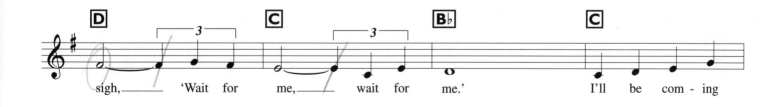

sigh,_____ 'Wait for me,_____ wait for me.' I'll be com - ing

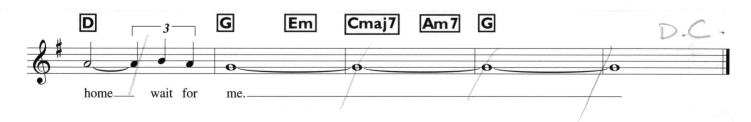

D.C.

home_____ wait for me._____

WHEN YOU TELL ME THAT YOU LOVE ME

Words & Music by Albert Hammond & John Bettis

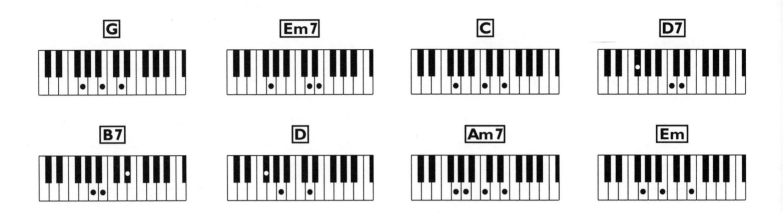

Voice: **Strings**

Rhythm: **16 beat**

Tempo: ♩ = 84

I wan-na call the stars down from the sky, I wan-na

live a day that ne-ver dies. I wan-na change the world on-ly for

you, all the im-pos-si-ble I wan-na do. I wan-na

hold you close un-der the rain, I wan-na kiss your smile and feel your

pain,   I know what's beau - ti - ful look - ing at

you,   in a world of lies you are the truth. And ba - by

ev - 'ry time you touch me,   I be - come a he - ro, I'll make you safe no mat - ter where you

are   and bring you ev - 'ry-thing you ask for,   no - thing is a - bove me,   I'm

shin - ing like a can - dle in the dark   when you tell me that you love_____ me.

You love_____ me,   when you tell me that you

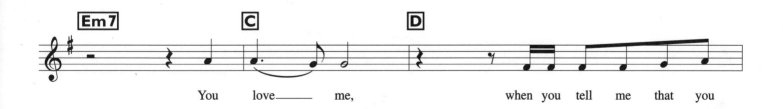

love   me._____

WITHOUT YOU

Words & Music by Peter Ham & Tom Evans

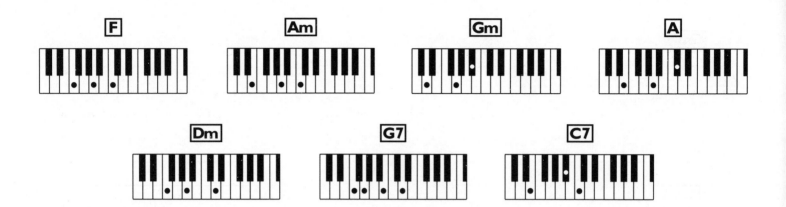

Voice: **Trumpet**

Rhythm: **Ballad**

Tempo: ♩ = 69

No I can't for-get this ev-'ning or your

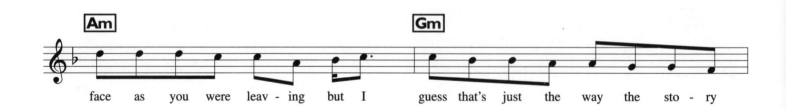

face as you were leav-ing but I guess that's just the way the sto-ry

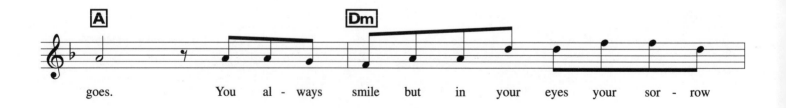

goes. You al-ways smile but in your eyes your sor-row

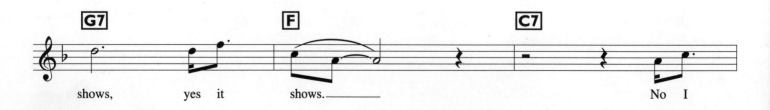

shows, yes it shows.___ No I

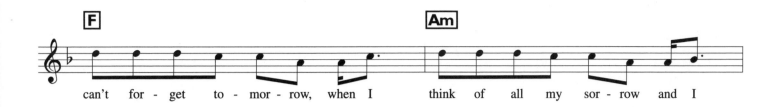

can't for-get to-mor-row, when I think of all my sor-row and I

had you there but then I let you go. And now it's on-ly fair that I should let you

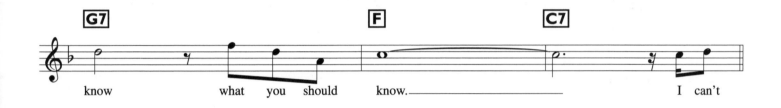

know what you should know. I can't

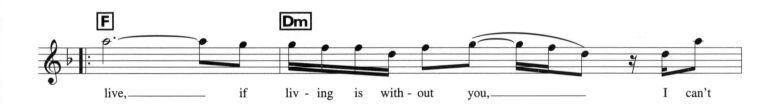

live, if liv-ing is with-out you, I can't

live, I can't give a-ny-more. I can't

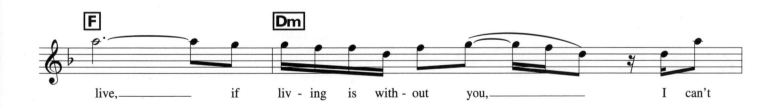

live, if liv-ing is with-out you, I can't

Repeat to fade

give, I can't give a-ny-more. I can't

WONDERWALL

Words & Music by Noel Gallagher
© Copyright 1995 Oasis Music/Creation Songs Limited/Sony/ATV Music Publishing,
10 Great Marlborough Street, London W1.

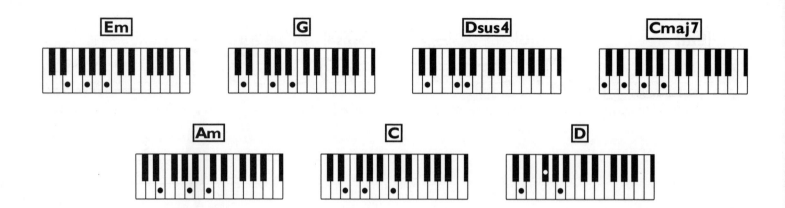

Voice: **Trumpet**

Rhythm: **Soft Rock**

Tempo: ♩ = 90

To - day   is gon - na be the day   that they're gon - na throw it back   to   you.—

By now you should've somehow re - a - lised what you got - ta   do.—   I don't be - lieve that   a - ny - bo - dy

feels   the way I   do——   a - bout   you   now.————

Back - beat   the word was on the street   that the   fi - re   in your heart   is   out.—

I'm sure you've heard it all be-fore, but you ne-ver real-ly had a doubt.—

I don't be - lieve— that a - ny-bo - dy feels the way I do— a-bout you now.

_____ And all—— the roads— we have— to walk— are wind-

- ing, and all——— the lights— that lead— us there— are blind - ing.

There are ma - ny things that I— would like to say to you,— but I don't know how.——

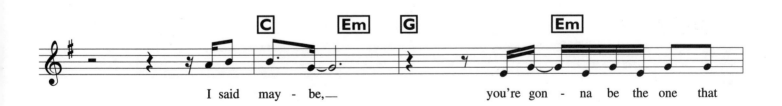

I said may - be,— you're gon - na be the one that

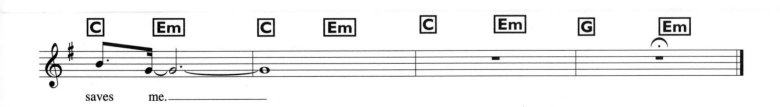

saves me._____

WORDS

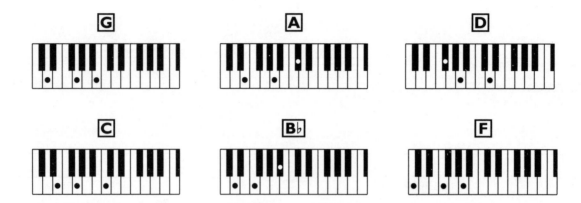

Voice: **Clarinet**

Rhythm: **Ballad**

Tempo: ♩ = 92

Smile an ev - er - last - ing

smile, a smile could bring you near to me. Don't

ev - er let me find you gone, 'cause that would bring a tear to me.

This world has lost it's glo - ry, let's start a brand new sto - ry

now, my love. Right now, there'll be no oth-er time and I can show you how, my

love.— Talk in ev-er-last-ing words and de-di-cate them all to me.

And I will give you all my life, I'm here if you should call to me.

You think that I don't ev-en mean a sin-gle word I say.

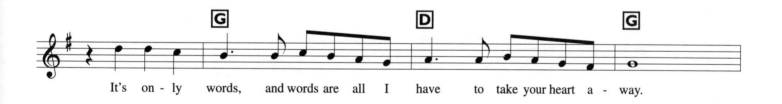

It's on-ly words, and words are all I have to take your heart a-way.

It's on-ly words, and words are all I have to take your heart a-way.

It's on-ly words, and words are all I have to take your heart a-way.